About the Author

Isabella Ritchie is now the author of *Can You Hear Me Now?* which is pretty evident as you're reading her book now. When she isn't hauled up in her bedroom reading and writing Isabella spends her time travelling the world, eating pasta, using sarcasm as her natural defence and most importantly coddling her dog, who is by far her favourite member of her family.

Can You Hear Me Now?

Isabella Ritchie

Can You Hear Me Now?

Olympia Publishers
London

www.olympiapublishers.com
OLYMPIA PAPERBACK EDITION

A CIP catalogue record for this title is
available from the British Library.

ISBN: 978-1-80439-114-3

This is a work of fiction.
Names, characters, places and incidents originate from the writer's
imagination. Any resemblance to actual persons, living or dead, is
purely coincidental.

First Published in 2023

Olympia Publishers
Tallis House
2 Tallis Street
London
EC4Y 0AB

Printed in Great Britain

Dedication

To my beautiful mum for believing I could, when everyone else made me feel as though I couldn't. Thank you for holding my hand through the light and the dark.

You have no idea the kind of cruelty I had to face to become this understanding of the life that stands outside of rose-coloured lenses.

There never feels like a safe place once family betrays you.

Toys became weapons shaped like spears,
hugs became coffins used for restraint,
hands became a suffocating force that swiped away screams,
games became tactics used to manipulate the mind,
sundresses and skirts became gateways to an easier entrance,
layered clothes became armour to delay the inevitable
outcome.
My childhood
became a battleground of bloodshed.

What was so desirable about my body that had yet reached double digits?

Splintering pain crawls up my spine
but all is forgotten as I angle my head backwards
forgotten even as he tears at my underwear.
Her eyes scrutinise my own
leaving her humour to reflect against our blood that ties us
together.
Her laugh haunts the wind that swipes at my lungs.
Betrayal
betrayal
betrayal.

As his body caged mine
my mind flashed with recognition.
It's happening again.

Of course I blamed you
because if I couldn't stomach blaming them,
then who better to blame than the person I love most.

For a period that felt like a lifetime
I felt trapped behind the prison that was
your eyes.

I refuse to apologise for my actions that were caused by the agony you put me through.

I was seven the first time I was touched.
Her hands mercilessly scorned my body as she left behind a
trail of
confusion
agony
hatred
and forever a punishment laced with shame.
My eyes had burned and crackled as they began to glaze
over,
a sensation I would soon be more familiar with than that of
a smile.
And to this day I wonder if that same meticulous burn has
ever left me
or if the same scars she carved into the flesh of my skin will
forever bare the reminder of what I lost in those many
harrowing years.

Would you still love me with the lights on?

I was fourteen.
His lips tasted of starvation and his breath reeked of
alcohol,
which when it wafted against my nostrils they singed in
desperation.
His hands were harsh which he undoubtedly picked up from
his father,
the muffled cries coming from my own mouth blacked out
from his parent's grubby hands.
My screams,
wails
yelps,
signifying the women before me.
His urgency and decay of softness showed me I wasn't the
first
and was far from being the last.
Now I know where the saying
like father like son comes from.

I don't think I'll ever feel whole again,
not entirely.
I believe that one day I'll just be at peace with the missing
pieces
and maybe that will my salvation.

As the trousers at my waist that once sinched me tightly
hang at my hips loosely
my entire body buzzes with recognition.
Their eyes wander over the gauntness in my face and the
slice of untouched birthday cake
making my brain convulse with pride.
The lightbulb illuminates at the forefront of my mind
'They're finally noticing you.'

At what price did it take for you to become a man?
Because for your sole desperation for power you stole
everything soft and gentle right from under my feet.
Was the prize sweeter than honey?
Or sour like candy.
Did the prize become worth it whilst I was left with a price?
Do you feel powerful?
Do you feel brave?
Did you get a badge of honour for taking my pride?
Taking my soft edges and tearing them apart, rendering them
shattered like glass beneath my feet.
Do you feel like a man now?

How many battles do I need to be slaughtered in before it's acceptable for me to lose the war?

Love will forever be a myth if cowards like you wield the word.

The rims of her eyes glowed crimson
whilst her hands shook vigorously
tracing her battle scars
as she attempted to not start the war all over again.

Isn't it funny how we console people with the words we wished we were told?

Would she be proud of who I've become?
Or would she look at me like I'm a stranger?

With their heads out of the sand
I can see clearly
that they never loved me,
let alone cared enough to stand by me.

Would we share any less blood if I sliced it from my vein?

I killed myself inside and out to find the old me
only to find out she died a long time ago.

You look incredible!
You look stunning!
You look radiant!
You have to tell me your secret
though they never cared to mention the chunks of hair that
began to heap.
You look beautiful.
How do you do it?
Though their common eye never saw how every time I sat
up,
stood straight,
moved positions, my vision blurred, turning to stars.
You look so healthy now!
I wish I looked like you
though they could never understand why my nights had
shortened due to the bruising on my ribs.
Now they see the missing hair,
now they pick up on the fact I take an extra minute to
balance myself and when they decided on their own terms
to stare hard enough,
they noticed the bruising,
the prominent ribs,
hips,
collarbones,
cheekbones,
spine.
You look so ill.
You're so pale.
You look so unhealthy.
Why would you do that to yourself?
You were so beautiful.

You'll be okay.
You'll be okay.
You'll be okay.
His words cradled though doing nothing for the bile burning the back of my throat.
It's going to be fun.
It's going to be fun.
It's going to be fun.
But nothing felt fun about how his grip began to tighten, nothing felt fun about how his lips got hungrier viewing me as nothing but his prey.
Trust me.
Trust me.
Trust me.
Though trust wasn't built with his hand clamping my mouth as he silenced my screams, whilst my tears were made to speak volumes.
'Can we please do this another day?'
'Please stop.'
'You're hurting me, get off!'
'Let me leave.'
'Get off me.'
Please.
Please.
Please.
The words that rendered me useless as they were nothing but a roaring challenge for him as he gripped my waist and shoved my head further to the side.
Be quiet.
Shut up.
Stop moving.

Were the words he spat when he stole so much from me,
leaving me with the feeling of a battered corpse when he
dropped me to the floor
Demonstrating to me that I was little to nothing anymore
You'll be okay
Please
Be quiet
Were the words I turned around for myself as I amped the
tap to its boiling point, letting it scold my skin as I attempted
to scorch his touch from off of my body
You'll be okay
You'll be okay
You'll be okay
Has never felt the same since that day

Selfish
cowardly
weak winded
so many complex words were spat for what I had achieved
as
My Happily Ever After.
Though now I'm lying on my bathroom floor,
my body cold to the touch and achingly dull,
my pulse is no longer calculated.
In the distance a women's wails are penetrating someone
else's eardrums.
But now I'm happy
just somewhere else.

When I cry it feels like my soul is bleeding,
my heart is shattering
and my mind is imploding
amongst any thought that could corrupt me vividly.

My past doesn't need me,
no, of course not,
and I know full well that my future
is pining for me,
waiting for me to finally give in.
But my past
is so many things,
it held my hand throughout all of my dark nights,
intoxicating me with the contentment of not knowing who I
really am without it,
thriving off my misfortune
to slip into old habits that truly die hard.
So
who really needs fresh air
when I've survived long enough with the smoke that's
snuffing me out blissfully?
What's five more minutes?

For someone who never cried wolf
she sure was berated for her cries.

I found a sense of
consistency
in their violence, and for a child who couldn't afford safety I
was starving for something of substance.

'Abuse can feel like love',
five words that reach deep inside of my soul and tear up
years of hard work
because it's overwhelmingly true that her abuse could feel
like love.
Though her love was a coin toss,
some days she would eat with me at lunch and ask me to
play with her friends,
the simplicity of it would make me grin for a mile,
I'd laugh with her,
she'd made me laugh,
she'd tell me I was the best cousin she could ever ask for,
and the little voice inside of my head grew twice its size,
telling me this time,
this time it would be different,
she would love me.
Then the coin would drop,
her laugh would seep an octave,
she'd isolate me,
making sure no one would bat me an eyelash,
she'd wake me up with her hands down my pants,
ignoring my pleas as she passed.
Her torture wouldn't stop until my tears stained the pillows
underneath my head.
Then when she did stop
she'd laugh,
then again,
repeat,
again,
repeat.
She mimicked my hope.

My love and care like a ballerina attached to the strings she
toyed with
up until those rose-coloured glasses were smashed to
smithereens.
She smiled
I smiled
she laughed
I laughed
she smirked
I cried
she tainted
I dimmed.
"I love you."
"I love you too."

Silence.
Silence.
Silence.
She wipes my tears,
holds my hand,
cradles the darkness.
Silence.
Silence.
Silence.
She's the only peace I've found
despite her memorising every heinous event like the back of
her palm.
She didn't judge.
There were no questions asked.
Silence.
Silence.
Silence.
She may have consequences
but she's safe,
she's consistent and has no lashings of temper,
her voice is soft and lulling as she strolls alongside me.
We walk at my pace,
reminding me that the thoughts need to stay kind.
Silence.
Silence.
Silence.
My protection after the harm.

Loving you was like
strapping a blade to my heart
and allowing you to make
every terrorising move you saw fit.

I told my friends,
family,
strangers, I was smitten when I dated my first boyfriend,
I told them all about the notes we'd send to one another,
our texts that would start from the crack of dawn until the
depths of the night.
How your hands would play with my hair,
how you'd draw circles on my arms,
how you would take me to meet his best friend,
how you invited me to watch fireworks with you,
how you would text me cute things after a stressful day,
how you would call me on your dog walks,
how you'd cuddle me whilst I showed you my favourite
movies.
How you told me you loved,
cherished,
adored me,
how you'd say the sweetest things and for a few seconds I
believed it,
up until that night.
You changed so drastically
that I wondered if it was my fault.
Did I become too unavailable?
Did the alcohol make me too tempting?
Did that then make my clothes too inviting?
Did I do something wrong?
You changed so much that night that you catastrophically
dragged me down with you.
We both morphed into different people after the clock
struck seven.
One with their will in fact
another with sheer cruelty.

So many fingertips tripped over my skin,
so many hands claimed my body as their own,
so many palms threatened my privacy,
making grotesque trembles become a sense of normalcy.
Even though that realisation,
the fact I was so desensitized to another's hands taking
whatever they wished, without a second thought to wipe
away my consent like a spec of dirt,
that wasn't the reality that disturbed me the most.
The thing that left me mortified,
devastated beyond repair, was the fact that in the end when I
woke up in a state of terror and despair
I wasn't able to decipher whose hands I was petrified of.

You all forget
that I didn't want to be the
strong
little
girl.
I didn't want to be known as
the brave one either,
the one they idolised with their foolish words that they had
considered compliments.
I didn't want to be the girl who got told they're an old soul,
I didn't ever want to be told throughout how mature I was,
how mature I was becoming.
I didn't want to have to be strong
nor brave back then,
and I sure as hell don't want to be any of those things now.
I want to crumble,
fall, splinter,
and maybe even shatter.
And this time around
I might even want someone to glue my pieces back together
though over time everyone forgets that I'm suffering,
leaving me stranded in the mud
that was really quicksand,
devouring me wholly,
one by one.
Because I'm brave,
because I'm strong,
you all forget.

Everyone says there's nothing wrong with me,
yet you chose her over me,
you did it until infinity.
Why couldn't one of those universes align with mine?

My mind withered away into a merciless numb escape that
exerted throughout the entirety of my body.
Over time
I couldn't help but be infatuated with the blood that
flickered down my thighs,
my hands shaking vigorously as I watched each intricately
cut newfound scar start to form at my own causing,
mimicking the plethora of old scars surrounding the new.
Each drop of blood helping to ground me,
reminding me I was breathing,
that I was indeed alive,
reminding me that the blood that coursed throughout my
veins was in fact still pumping accordingly,
reminding me that the feeling of being completely and
utterly infatuated with my mind and body's numbness was
exactly that,
a feeling.

I collected courage like pennies,
spent them like a goldmine,
then used my rations to plummet to rock bottom.

What was it about me that made you hate my tainted heart, when all I did was make it bleed for you?

I don't have an eating disorder.
I don't wake up famished.
But,
of course, I regularly see how long I can go without food.
How long it will take until stars cloud my eyes,
how long it will take until minutes pass and I'm still trying to
stand up from my seat,
how many hours will pass until my body feels as though it
can be taken away by the wind.
But I don't have an eating disorder,
I don't obsess about the intake of my food,
I just like to check my meals on a scale sometimes,
I find it intriguing to know the calories,
sugar,
carbs,
salt,
fat, and occasionally the potassium.
But you see
sometimes I'm just curious to see how drastically the scale
can change throughout twenty-four hours.
I rarely check more than twenty times a day.
It's just my competitive nature that has me jotting down my
meals compared to the rest of my family to see if the
calories I consume can plummet to half of theirs.
But I don't have an eating disorder.
What does it matter if I look in the mirror every time I get
up and go to the bathroom,
my bed,
downstairs,
outside,
to the shops?

In school,
college,
it doesn't matter that what I see makes me feel sick to my
stomach.
Everyone loses their appetite in odd ways
and
it means nothing when I tell my friends and family I've eaten
when I've maybe missed a meal
or three.
I'm not ill like everyone's trying to tell me I am.
I don't need their petrified gazes that shine with pity.
I don't have an eating disorder.

I wish you had snuffed me out
with the same hands you used
to smother my screams.

What about me?
I was used to being the dark horse,
the one that was disregarded,
the one that said too much,
or often not enough.
The one who didn't quite click into the family dynamic,
the one that was too hot,
then far too cold,
the one that felt too much,
the one who was far too much in general.
I was also used to her being granted the spotlight.
I was used to her having every spec of attention
whilst always harvesting their worry
along with their thoughts and agendas.
She was the one that always said the right things,
she was the one who chose the puzzle pieces and forced
them to work,
the one that dictated the temperatures,
the ones whose feelings were always valid,
feelings that everyone protected.
She didn't only steal the spotlight,
the one that had people's heads turned and cranked solely to
her,
she also stole little pieces of me,
starting with their thoughts and speculations,
then their eyes,
then my hope,
then my joy,
lastly my innocence.

You speak about protecting me
as if I'm some special
little ornament you hang up on a shelf.
I can't help but be bitter
and resent you for doing so.
I can't help but realise all the things you didn't pay attention
to,
all the things that I endured
alone,
that in the end I blamed myself for.
Starting from her hands,
her objects she used on me for multiple years,
the same years I became her punching bag.
After all, she was abused too,
'So why not let it happen to you?'
The hands of three other boys who took
and took
and took.
I now know my truth
but
the truth isn't always something that sets you free.
Instead,
it holds the power to trap you,
and your truth is
you can't protect me because you never actually did.

I was a child who was forced to grow up.
I faced things that no normal child faced at such a young age
and although I was pried from my childhood,
I desperately clawed to the things that made my soul feel
fresh.
I surrounded myself with teddies
and a hundred different kinds of blankets for a sense of
security and safety that I never received from others.
I re-bought the dolls I threw out because the adults around
me jeered me with the words
'So grown',
'So mature.'
I would spend extra time in the toy section hoping I would
shrink, along with the years that I wished would subtract
instead of multiply.
I continuously tried to revisit my childhood,
attempting to take a closer look at the 'happier' version of
myself,
the one they all want back,
the untainted,
the undamaged parts of me.
But when I hold my teddies tight,
when I wrap myself up in blankets,
when I play the part of a young,
foolish,
pitiful child,
when I look into her eyes I'm greeted with the gruesome
fact, that she was never really happy,
she was continuously forced,
continuously pushed.
Shoved.

Her dignity spat on like she was muck under another's shoe.
She wasn't joyful.

She was controlled and used as a ploy,
her ignorance smothered with 'maturity' and 'purity', two
luxuries I could never afford.

I've read many of books,
poems,
sonnets,
lyrics from a thousand songs,
about lovers kissing away each other's pain.
Though I had kissed others,
many others,
half of the time their kisses smothered my pores with
nightmares and etched my mind with pure terror.
Other times they made me feel nothing,
so they could never kiss away my pain,
nor could I kiss and obliterate my own either.
But
I did kiss bottles of alcohol
and I swallowed,
sniffed,
and smoked my pain away.
Though I'll admit my methods had similarities with your
lovers,
in the end
they were all temporary,
and once the high dulls
you're left with that same pit of agony that you were once
so
desperately running away from.
This time around its different.
The pain splinters you blind.
You'll beg for that feeling again.
Sometimes you'll go back to it,
most of the time you'll go back for it,
because hell, those few hours,

minutes,
seconds,
they felt worth it
if it meant destroying yourself
over and over again.
Then so what?
It feels incredible whilst you're doing it,
indescribable,
the temporary pain becomes a crutch and my god that
crutch feels blissfully beautiful.
So if I can understand why you kiss your pain away,
why you lay down with that lover that leaves you black, blue
and bloody,
the lover that causes you nothing but the sweltering agony
that coops you inside of your mind.
Then can you try to understand that in the end we're really
just the same,
we were cut from the same double-edged cloth, though
tossed onto different pathways,
whilst I chose the right,
you chose the left.

My addiction was seeing my blood smeared over my thighs
watching as it dripped and splattered onto the achingly cold
floor.
I loved the sensation that radiated throughout me.
I was addicted to the action
along with the aftermath.
My tears would stop flooding when I saw and felt the
release,
when I released the feelings from my pores, when I finally
gave in to the heat that would radiate from my blood.
Don't ever mistake my actions,
I did it for myself,
I would always do it for myself.
I didn't want the attention or for anyone to look at me like
an invalid,
But I did enjoy the satisfaction of the shock that withered
over their faces for a split second.
I enjoyed the words that would find themselves lodged at the
back of their throats and I enjoyed finally having power over
a situation that I felt internally lost within.

An ulcer on the heart—
My words may have bite
as yours attempted to soothe the sores,
but when she told me she loved me
I believed her,
any child would.
So, when I mistook salt for sugar,
how do you expect me to warm to your plummeting
temperatures?
I made the mistake once
and with your words that wafer thin,
why would I ever chance frost bite to yet another pair of
identical-looking hands?

With knives in my underwear,
a machete to my skull,
all I can think is
'Aren't I too young for this?'

I hate you.
I hate how they cherish you,
how they adore you,
how they greedily smile at you and engulf you in like a
decadent desert.
It makes me internally shatter at the sight.
I compare myself to you.
So many others compare me to you too.
You're the living reminder that you're everything I'm not.
I glare at myself in the mirror,
pulling myself apart like picking a needle from a haystack.
I compare my laugh,
my smile,
the shade of green my eyes are,
my nose
my god I even compare the way I walk.
It's pitiful how much I envy you.
I hate how I'm second best to you,
how your achievements were thrown in my face whilst you
beat my innocence
bloody.
How you were always known as the kind,
lovely,
funny,
sweet,
family-orientated,
smooth-edged
one.
You were.
You are everything I cannot be.

I've learnt how to deal with the pain,
but that sole fact could never substitute the truth that I
never deserved it.
The pain I never talk about, the agony I never allow myself
to feel because the cold harsh reality of it manages to singe
my airways, leaving me lifeless to their touch.
I wore sundresses,
size seven,
eight,
nine.
In my children's clothes,
take a look at her face,
the tears that mar her skin,
the pain that would waver throughout her body when they
engrained the core memories into her childhood,
the desperate cries for help that were never answered,
the hopelessness
the callous truth that no one noticed what was happening.
His hands.
Her hands.
There was never a safe place once family betrayed me.

I wish someone noticed.
I wished someone looked me square in the eyes and told me
they could see the light draining from them.
I wished someone paid closer attention
and I wished someone saw me for who I was.
I wished they gave me the attentive gaze they gaze her,
but in the end their marks settled me for the black sheep.
Bravery plays a fierce force in my life,
a luxury some don't strive for.
So, I guess cowardice too plays a part in everyone's life,
and theirs are flooded with it

I never admitted it to myself,
to a friend,
to a parent,
to a sibling,
to anyone,
though I'm aware they assumed it.
Why wouldn't they?
But having those words leave my lips felt like another piece
of sanity escaping me,
it felt as though there were other parts of me that they still
controlled.
I thought that once it entered the past it was no longer
allowed to massacre the moments that were my own.
I was scared.
I was scared every time they touched me,
every time they raped me
every time they assaulted me.
I was so scared it paralysed my mind in every moment they
inflicted themselves upon me.
But most of all it scared me every day after that.
Maybe I feared them,
maybe I was simply just scared of the acts,
but I think I was truly just terrified of what they could take,
of whom they could take,
and every time they condemned my body to torture, they
took another little part of me away from myself.

I gave up trying to make it to the finish line before you
as my worth is no longer dependant on who sees me first.

There's so much blood on my hands,
so much blood on my thighs,
my wrists,
and most of all my heart.
But there's more on theirs,
they're haunted with my blood,
each of them.
Starting with her.
She tortured me for it at seven.
She's drowning in my blood.
Then him.
He tore it out of me at eight.
He's drowning in my blood.
Then he came along and ripped it out of me at fourteen.
He's drowning in my blood.
Lastly his hands crafted the knife used to stab me in the back
at sixteen.
He's drowning in my blood.
Well, you see I may be able to wash my hands,
my thighs,
my wrists,
and I may also be able to soothe the wounds tied to my
heart,
but the four of them will forever be tainted and stained.
My blood will ruin them whereas mine has cleansed me.

Was I really as bad as you made me out to be?
Were the words you spat,
spewed,
concocted,
truthful, or were you just biased to your agony?
Was the torment due to there being no one in hindsight you
could blame
but me?
Did the trauma stunt your level of empathy?
But in the end
we were the punching bag of our inattentiveness,
neglect,
and sorrow.
Were we really as bad as we made ourselves out to be?
Or did I really just need someone to blame?

Her sole presence alone sticks out like a sore thumb
among a meadow of seeds that have yet bloomed into
flowers,
though in my eyes
who would want to be a flower amongst a garden of thorns?

I will longer hate my tears because you weaponised your own.

No love is great enough to lose yourself in between.

If you blossomed and grew after the abuse it was never because the trauma made you stronger,
it was because despite it all you overcame and conquered,
it was because of your singular breaths that overturned roaring seas.
That was all you,
not them.

'It's time for you to let me go,'
the girl says,
her voice barely a whisper.
Tears run down my cheeks,
imitating that of race cars.
She stays silent as I hang on to the ghost of her.
She doesn't realise how much I miss her,
how much I want her,
how much I need her.
'I need you to let me go. You know I'm not really here. You
know I'm never coming back,'
she reiterates.
This time her voice wobbles.
It sounds so similar that I swore in the next beat I heard my
heart crack behind its cage.
I think about telling her I can't let her go
I don't want to as without her I'll never know if I'll be okay.
'Please let me go. I need you too. You need to let me go,'
she pleads.
This time her voice is further away.
My mind withers.
I do as she says.
I hold my breath.
'One last request.'
I speak to her with no response.
I place the picture of me
at seven years old
back in the photo album.
'Be free.'

It'll always be okay to cry over the trauma you once thought you had left behind.

Her bravery was resilience
as for every day that passed whether she stood tall or
crumbled to the floor,
she endured.

I wish I could have said goodbye.
I wish I could have held you in my arms and sang you a
lullaby.
I wish I could have dried your tears
and swept away all of your pain for a thousand years.
I wish I could have drawn circles on your hands
to then bury away your bleeding heart beneath the sand.
I wish I could have coddled you dearly,
telling you stories of a life lived fiercely.
I wish I could have given you our love,
to remind you that you'll always be my little dove.

There's nothing wrong with you.
You settle for those who can only handle less
when you're so much more.

To heal is to care,
to understand,
to be empathetic,
to be resilient,
to listen and learn,
to reflect,
to be sympathetic,
to be kind and gentle,
to start and then stop,
to sometimes feel as though your progress has been
destroyed.
Each of these steps start with
yourself.

Your emotions paint your life with purpose,
the catastrophic and brilliant.
Don't let anyone tell you they're too much.

I was lost for a time that felt like an eternity,
but suddenly when it all went dark
I saw a tiny little light.
Home.

'Five to thirty eight'
I remember you
I remember your presence at the end of my bed
I remember your hands in my hair
Your lips wrapped in the strands
Your fingers on my pyjama bottoms
The same callouses that later travelled under the band of my
underwear
I remember the way you followed me around with a smile
I remember your eyes
Your nose that inhaled my scent
Your skin that lingered on my own
Your body
Every part of it that mottled my flesh as you stripped me to
the bone
I remember you
I remember what you did to me
I remember it all.